D0353305

Snowy the Snowman

Sticker & Activity Fun

igloobooks

Letter to Santa

It's nearly Christmas! Write Santa a letter asking for what you want.
You can also draw a picture of your perfect present.

First Snow

The first snowfall is always an exciting time of year. Can you spot seven differences between picture A and picture B?

A

B

Answers on page 16

Winter What?

It's fun to play in the snow. Join the dots and find out what the children have made in the snow.

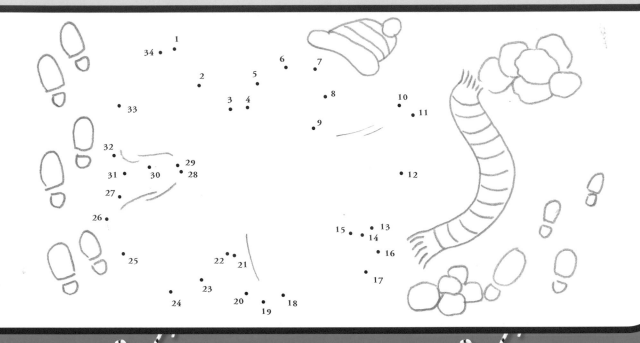

Toy Shop Puzzle

At Christmas time the shops are full of lots of lovely gifts. Find the missing pieces of the jigsaw. Which piece is the odd one out?

A
B
C
D

Answers on page 16

Snowman Maker

Design your own Snowy the Snowman in the space below
and then use your best pens to decorate it.

Party Time

Help the children find their way to the Christmas party?
Why not visit Snowy the Snowman on the way?

START

END

Answers on page 16

Snowy Paper Chain

Follow the steps below and make your own paper-chain decoration.

You will need:

Pencil   Card   Scissors

Top Tip

Why not try different Christmas characters, such as elves and Santa?

① Fold the sheet of card into thirds.

② While the card is folded, draw a picture of a snowman. Behind the snowman, across the middle, draw a rectangle shape from one side to the other.

Use your best pens to decorate the snowman and the rectangle.

③

④ Ask an adult to cut around the snowman and rectangle. Unfold the card and you should have three snowmen joined together.

The Christmas Eve Bedtime Game

You will need:
2–4 players
A dice, coins
for counters.

START

1

Get hit by
a snowball.
Miss a turn.

17   **16**   Feed the reindeer. Miss a turn.   **14**   **13**

18

19   Lose your scarf. Go back three spaces.   **21**   Slide across the ice. Go forward two spaces.   **23**

How to play

Place your counters on the start square. Each player takes turns to roll the dice and move their counter the number rolled. If your counter lands on an action square, read it out and follow the instructions. You must roll the exact number to land on the finish square. First player to the finish square wins!

3

4

Pop in a toyshop. Go back two places.

6

7

8

12

11

Find a shortcut. Go forward three places.

9

24

See Santa on his sleigh. Go back two spaces.

26

FINISH

Christmas Cards

Everyone likes a bright and festive Christmas card this time of year.
Use your best pens and decorate the cards below.

Trees of Trinkets

You don't want to forget anything this Christmas. Study the decorated trees for 20 seconds then turn over and answer the quiz questions.

Chocolate Treats

At Christmas you get to eat lots of festive treats. Pair up the chocolates below? Which chocolate doesn't have a partner?

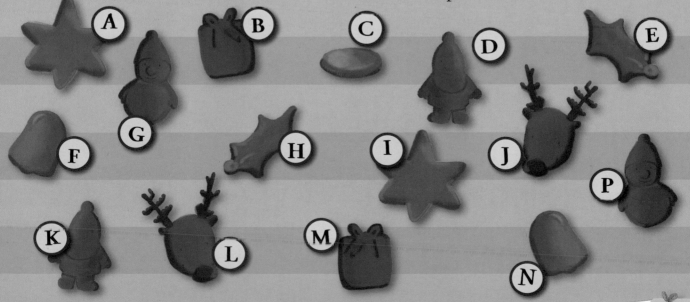

Answers on page 16

Trees of Trinkets Quiz

You've studied the Christmas trees from the previous page, now answer the questions below. And remember, no peeking!

1. How many stars were there?

2. What was on the fourth tree?

3. How many baubles were on the third tree?

4. How many trees had tinsel?

Close Up Crackers

At Christmas you always get the chance to pull a cracker and discover a surprise gift. Can you match the close-up pictures with the correct crackers?

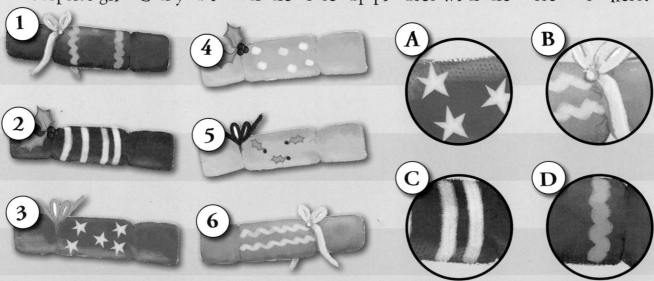

Answers on page 16

Christmas Lights Show

Santa has come to turn on the town's Christmas lights. Look at the picture below and answer the questions at the bottom of the page.

The Big
Christmas Light Up

Answers on page 16

1. How many stars can you count?

2. How many scarves can you spot?

3. How many reindeer are there?

Shadowy Snowmen

When the snowfall is heavy, it is fun to make a snowman.
Can you find the owner of the snowman shadow below?

A

B

C

D

Sneaky Creaky

Can you help Billy sneak along the creaky corridor so he can get downstairs? Only step on the odd-numbered floorboards.

Answers on page 16

Whose Presents?

It's Christmas morning and Santa has delivered lots of presents, but none of them have gift tags. Follow the clues to work out which present is for which child.

CLUES

1. Michael's present has a pink bow and green wrapping paper.

2. Dylan's present has a blue bow and purple wrapping paper.

3. Rachel's present has purple wrapping paper and has a purple bow.

A

B

C

D

E

F

G

H

Answers on page 16

Answers

Page 3: First Snow

Page 4: Winter What?

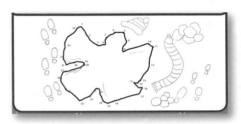

Page 4: Toy Shop Puzzle

Pieces A, B and D complete the puzzle. Piece C is the odd one out.

Page 6: Party Time

Page 11: Chocolate Treats

A and I, B and M, , D and K, E and H, F and N, G and P. C is the odd one out.

Page 12: Trees of Trinkets

1. There are 11 stars.
2. The fourth tree has candle decorations.
3. There are four baubles on the third tree.
4. Two trees have tinsel.

Page 12: Close Up Crackers

A-3, B-6, C-2 and D-1.

Page 13: Christmas Lights Show

1. There are 16 stars.
2. There are 6 scarves.
3. There is one reindeer.

Page 14: Shadowy Snowmen

Snowman A.

Page 14: Sneaky Creaky

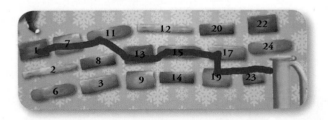

Page 15: Whose Presents?

Michael is getting present H
Dylan is getting present D
Rachel is getting present B